3

The children were messy.

The children were noisy.

The children were silly.

The children were untidy.

'Oh dear!' said Mrs May.

'It's the weather.'

The children were cross.

The children were grumpy.

The children were unhappy.

'Oh dear!' said Mrs May.

'It's the weather.'

The sun was shining.

The children were good.

'What a day!' said Mrs May.